SOMETHING UNDER THE BED IS DROOLING

A Calvin and Hobbes Collection by Bill Watterson
Foreword by Pat Oliphant

A TRUMPET CLUB SPECIAL EDITION

Published by The Trumpet Club
666 Fifth Avenue, New York, New York 10103

Calvin and Hobbes® is syndicated internationally by Universal Press Syndicate.

Copyright © 1988 by Bill Watterson

ISBN: 0-440-84653-6

This edition published by arrangement with Andrews and McMeel,
a Universal Press Syndicate Company
Printed in the United States of America
October 1991

10 9 8 7 6 5 4 3 2 1
CUS

Foreword

There is a mystical quality to Bill Watterson's work. What we have here is no mere comic strip. It possesses a dimension which was found once upon a time in George Herriman's Krazy Kat and, later, in Walt Kelly's Pogo. That, however, was long ago, and since their passing, there has been nothing in the world of cartoon art to replace them. Now, we have Calvin and Hobbes.

There are no mealy-mouths or namby-pamby characters in this strip. The kid is delightfully and dedicatedly rotten. The mother and the father (no names are given or necessary) live alongside their offspring in a state of agitated wonderment at what they must have done to deserve this child. The kid, for his part, lives a good 70 percent of his time in a world I remember well from my own childhood, peopled with unspeakable creatures of the imagination, and the rest of the time in a real world peopled with other unspeakables (the teacher, the girl, the school thug). Refuge from the latter world is found in the former. And then there's the goofy stuffed tiger. A gentle soul, he is much smarter than the kid, whose brashness he leavens with a wry, endearing wisdom.

There are many comic strips out there, a few good, some average, a great many merely background clutter. All have their own cast of characters, engaging or not, all glued and patched together with dialogue, some good, some not. Very few bright stars appear who possess that peculiar magic which can provoke comparison with the best of the past. Looking at the work of our two comparisons, Herriman and Kelly, we can see a wedding of idea and art rarely seen these days, a feeling that words can enhance art and art can do the same for the written — that a carefully wrought blend of these ingredients can create a degree of enchantment which bespeaks genius.

You want magic?

Watterson the alchemist has conjured forth a work of subtlety, character, and depth far out of proportion to his tender years. I wish him long life, and may the powers of his sorcery never diminish.

You want magic?

This is a collection of the sorcerer's recipes for changing simple ink and paper into the purest gold. Humbly allow me to present Calvin (the kid) and Hobbes (the tiger). This book is magic.

— PAT OLIPHANT

To Mom and Dad

I SAW A TURTLE DOWN BY THE CREEK.

BIG DEAL! WHO CARES? I'VE SEEN HUNDREDS OF TURTLES! PROBABLY MILLIONS! WHO WANTS TO SEE ANOTHER DUMB OL' TURTLE?

HA!

CAN I RIDE IN THE GROCERY CART?

I THINK YOU'RE A LITTLE BIG FOR THAT NOW.

PLEASE??

ALL RIGHT. UP YOU GO.

OH BOY!

NOW RUN DOWN THE AISLE AND LET GO!

AAWWEEEAWWEEAAW!

THE WATER LOOKED A LITTLE COLD, EH, TARZAN?

7

CALVIN and HOBBES
by WATTERSON

WANNA TOSS THE OL' PIGSKIN AROUND?

HECK NO.

PHOOEY.

THE CENTER SNAPS THE BALL!

THE QUARTERBACK LOOKS FOR AN OPENING!

THE DEFENSE DISINTEGRATES BENEATH THE COMING ONSLAUGHT! THE QUARTER-BACK JUMPS AND DODGES!

HOBBES BREAKS CLEAR!

CALVIN PASSES!

AN AMAZING CATCH! HOBBES IS AT THE 30 ... THE 20 ... THE 10 ...

... BUT HE'S TACKLED FROM BEHIND AND LATERALS TO CALVIN SO *HE* CAN MAKE THE TOUCHDOWN!

BUT CALVIN FUMBLES THE BALL AND HOBBES RECOVERS IT!

BUT A PENALTY IS CALLED ON THE PLAY AND HOBBES IS SENT TO THE BENCH!

HOBBES DEFECTS TO THE OTHER TEAM AND IS GREETED WITH ENTHUSIASTIC CHEERS! THE CROWD GOES WILD!

CALVIN PREPARES TO CRIPPLE THE TRAITOR WITH AN ILLEGAL FACE MASK PULL!

HOBBES DEFIES HIM BY POURING OUT HIS MOUTH GUARD ONTO CALVIN'S HELMET!

BOY, YOU CAN SEE WHY FOOTBALL IS SUCH A VIOLENT GAME!

HOBBES' TEAM GAINS A YARD! ALL THE CHEER-LEADERS COME OUT FOR SMOOCHES!!

9

WITH A DRINK OF MAGIC ELIXIR, CALVIN TURNS HIMSELF INVISIBLE.

COMPLETELY TRANSPARENT, HE ROAMS UNDETECTED!

CALVIN?

BOY, AS SOON AS YOU WANT SOMETHING DONE AROUND HERE, THAT KID'S NOWHERE TO BE SEEN.

HA HA! I HAVE TURNED MYSELF INVISIBLE!

BY REMOVING MY CLOTHING, I CAN PERPETRATE ANY CRIME UNDETECTED!

I HAVE COMPLETE FREEDOM! I CAN GET AWAY WITH ANYTHING!

CALVIN! WHAT ON EARTH ARE YOU DOING IN THE COOKIE JAR WITHOUT YOUR CLOTHES ON?!?

YOUR POLLS ARE SLIPPING, DAD. BETTER GET WITH IT.

CALVIN, BEING YOUR DAD IS NOT AN ELECTED POSITION. I DON'T HAVE TO RESPOND TO POLLS.

NOT ELECTED? YOU MEAN YOU CAN GOVERN WITH DICTATORIAL IMPUNITY?

EXACTLY.

IN SHORT, OPEN REVOLT AND EXILE IS THE ONLY HOPE FOR CHANGE?

I DON'T LIKE THE DIRECTION THIS CONVERSATION IS TAKING..

calvin and Hobbes
by WATTERSON

GRAVITY IS ARBITRARY!

CALVIN WAKES UP ONE DAY TO FIND HE IS IMMUNE TO THE FORCE OF GRAVITY.

HE HANGS ON TO THE GROUND FOR DEAR LIFE, BUT HIS GRIP IS WEAKENING!

HE CAN'T HOLD ON! HE... HE **LETS GO!**

HIGHER AND HIGHER, AS UPWARD HE FALLS!

ONLY BY GRABBING THE TAIL FIN OF A PASSING JET DOES CALVIN SAVE HIMSELF FROM BEING HURLED OUT INTO SPACE!

NO, NO, LET HIM FINISH. THIS IS VERY INTERESTING. SO AFTER YOU LANDED IN PHOENIX, WHAT HAPPENED?

WELL, I DON'T CARE. I'M NOT SEWING VELCRO ON THE OUTSIDE OF ALL HIS CLOTHES.

WELL, ABOUT THEN MY GRAVITY CAME BACK, SO I...

11

CRASH!

IT JUMPED ME!!

LOOK, THERE'S A FROG!

C'MON, LET'S CATCH IT!

I'M NOT GETTING NEAR IT.

WHY NOT?

THEY DRINK WATER ALL DAY JUST IN CASE SOMEONE PICKS THEM UP.

I'M GOING TO HANG AROUND THE DRUGSTORE ALL AFTERNOON AND EAT CANDY AND READ COMIC BOOKS!

OH, NO, YOU'RE NOT!

WHY NOT?!

BECAUSE I'M YOUR MOTHER AND I SAID SO. GET BACK IN HERE.

AND YOU CAN STOP GOOSE-STEPPING AROUND THE HOUSE!

HEY, MOM, CAN WE GO OUT FOR PIZZA TONIGHT?

NO, WE HAD PIZZA LAST NIGHT, AND BESIDES, IT'S TOO EXPENSIVE TO EAT OUT ALL THE TIME.

OH, YOU'D RATHER BLOW THE EVENING COOKING AND WASHING DISHES THAN SPEND A FEW BUCKS?

IT SEEMS LIKE WE GO OUT FOR PIZZA A LOT THESE DAYS.

IF YOU'D RATHER FIX A DISH OF CEREAL AT HOME BE MY GUEST.

HOBBES WANTS TRIPLE ANCHOVIES.

CALVIN AND HIS TRUSTY NAVIGATOR HOBBES ROAR DOWN THE RESIDENTIAL ROAD AT 90 M.P.H!

HOBBES PUTS ON THE TURN SIGNAL.

FASTER AND FASTER THEY GO! A BUSLOAD OF SCHOOLCHILDREN DIVES FROM THE SIDEWALK!

HOBBES PUTS ON THE WINDSHIELD WIPERS.

THE POLICE ARE AFTER THEM! CALVIN CRAWLS DOWN TO PUT IN THE CLUTCH AND SHIFT!

HOBBES STEERS AND BLOWS THE HORN!

ALL RIGHT, I'M BACK ALREADY! CAN'T I EVEN RUN AN ERRAND WITHOUT YOU BLOWING THE HORN ACROSS THE PARKING LOT?!

IT WAS HOBBES, MOM. NOT ME.

16

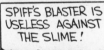

19

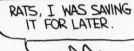

MICKEY MOUSE PANTS?!? YOU DON'T LOOK COOL! YOU LOOK LIKE AN IDIOT!

24

HERE COMES SUSIE. I'M GOING TO THROW A PINE CONE AT HER.

WWHIPPPP

POW!

ZINGGG

WATTERSON

YAHH!

OOF! GRRR!

RR!

RGH!

RRR!

UH! UH! RRR! UMPH!

TOUCHDOWN!

LET'S PLAY SOMETHING ELSE.

WATTERSON

ARE THERE ANY MONSTERS UNDER MY BED TONIGHT?

NO. NOPE. NO.

WATTERSON

IF THERE *WERE* ANY MONSTERS UNDER MY BED, HOW BIG WOULD THEY BE?

VERY SMALL. GO TO SLEEP.

MOMM!

26

WITH GREAT EFFORT, CALVIN THE HUMAN INSECT ADVANCES THE PAPER IN THE TYPEWRITER.

HIS ONLY HOPE FOR PROPER MEDICAL TREATMENT LIES IN HIS ABILITY TO WRITE A LEGIBLE MESSAGE TO HIS FAMILY!

HE CRAWLS TO EACH KEY AND JUMPS!

WHO WROTE "HELP I'M A BUG" ON MY LETTER TO GRANDMA?

EVIDENTLY SOME BUG. HOW STRANGE.

BACK AND FORTH.

BACK AND FORTH.

TIDAL WAVE!

BEATS ME, MOM. MAYBE THE SEAL AROUND THE TUB LEAKS.

WHAT'S THIS MUSIC?

IT'S "THE 1812 OVERTURE."

I KINDA LIKE IT. INTERESTING PERCUSSION SECTION.

THOSE ARE CANNONS.

AND THEY PERFORM THIS IN CROWDED CONCERT HALLS?? GEE, I THOUGHT CLASSICAL MUSIC WAS BORING!

WERE THERE DINOSAURS WHEN YOU WERE A KID, DAD?

OH SURE! YOUR GRANDFATHER AND I USED TO PUT ON OUR LEOPARD SKINS AND HUNT BRONTOSAURUS FOR **ALL** THE CLAN RITUALS.

LISTEN, BUSTER, I THINK CALVIN'S GRADES ARE BAD ENOUGH **ALREADY**, DON'T YOU?

THE HORRIFYING TYRANNOSAURUS LUMBERS ACROSS THE PREHISTORIC VALLEY.

THE MIGHTY DINOSAUR IS A WALKING DEATH MACHINE!

ONLY ONE OTHER CREATURE DARES TO CHALLENGE THE TERRIBLE TYRANNOSAURUS!

...THE SAVAGE *SABER-TOOTHED TIGER!*

UNK GZZ...

GG *MMF* YOW GZZZ

MKN GBZZ..YOW...

WAKE UP!

THE MEEK TYRANNOSAURUS, VICTIM OF AN INNOCENT MISUNDERSTANDING, TEARS LIKE HECK ACROSS THE PREHISTORIC VALLEY..

29

TOMORROW WE'RE GOING TO DISCUSS "CURRENT EVENTS" IN SCHOOL.

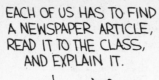

EACH OF US HAS TO FIND A NEWSPAPER ARTICLE, READ IT TO THE CLASS, AND EXPLAIN IT.

WHAT ARTICLE DID YOU CHOOSE?

THIS ONE.

"SPACE ALIEN WEDS TWO-HEADED ELVIS CLONE."

ACTUALLY, THERE'S NOT MUCH LEFT TO EXPLAIN.

LOOK WHAT YOU CAN DO WITH BIG SOCKS!

JUST PUT ONE OVER EACH EAR, AND ONE OVER YOUR NOSE...

AN ELEPHANT! HA HA! I WANT SOME SOCKS TOO!

IF I MISS THE BUS, IT'S GOING TO BE UNPLEASANT AROUND HERE!

CALVIN, HOW DID YOU BREAK THIS DISH?!

I WAS CARRYING TOO MUCH AND IT DROPPED.

YOUR PROBLEM IS YOU'VE GOT NO COMMON SENSE.

I'VE GOT **PLENTY** OF COMMON SENSE!

I JUST CHOOSE TO IGNORE IT.

I DON'T UNDERSTAND THIS BUSINESS ABOUT DEATH.

IF WE'RE JUST GOING TO DIE, WHAT'S THE POINT OF LIVING?

WELL, THERE'S SEAFOOD...

I DON'T KNOW WHY I EVEN *TALK* TO YOU BEFORE DINNER.

I'VE DECIDED I WANT TO BE A MILLIONAIRE WHEN I GROW UP.

WELL, YOU'LL HAVE TO WORK PRETTY HARD TO GET A MILLION DOLLARS.

NO, I WON'T. YOU WILL.

ME?

I JUST WANT TO INHERIT IT.

THE WORST PART ABOUT GOING TO SCHOOL IS WAITING FOR THE BUS.

ALL YOU CAN DO IS STAND HERE AND IMAGINE WHAT'S GOING TO GO WRONG DURING THE DAY. I BET WE HAVE A POP MATH QUIZ OR SOMETHING.

WELL, HERE COMES THE BUS. THANKS FOR WAITING WITH ME.

MY PLEASURE.

BOY, MY LUNCH BOX SEEMS LIGHT.

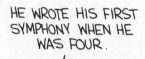

LOOK, MOM, I PUT ALL MY CLOTHES FOR TOMORROW ON THE STAIRS.

THEN IN THE MORNING, I'LL RUN OUT IN MY UNDERWEAR AND SLIDE DOWN AT TOP SPEED!

IF I AIM GOOD, I GO RIGHT INTO MY PANTS WHILE I'M PUTTING ON MY SHIRT, AND BY THE BOTTOM, I'M ALL DRESSED FOR SCHOOL!

WATTERSON

AND IF YOU PUT MY CEREAL ON THE STAIRS TOO, I WON'T HAVE TO GET UP UNTIL 30 SECONDS BEFORE THE BUS COMES.

FORGET IT, CALVIN.

ACK   IGG

LOOK, MOM, I'VE GOT RABIES.

GO SPIT OUT YOUR TOOTHPASTE AND STOP BEING SILLY.

MAYBE DAD WILL FALL FOR IT IF I BITE HIM FIRST.

WATTERSON

38

OOG, I FEEL AWFUL.

IF SOMEONE EVEN MENTIONS "MILK DUDS," I'M GONNA BARF.

ANOTHER HALLOWEEN COME AND GONE.

IT'S ALWAYS SUCH A LETDOWN AFTER A HOLIDAY.

WE MIGHT AS WELL GO INTO TOWN AND LOOK AT THE CHRISTMAS DECORATIONS.

MOM'S NOT FEELING WELL, SO I'M MAKING HER A "GET WELL" CARD.

THAT'S THOUGHTFUL OF YOU.

SEE, ON THE FRONT IT SAYS, "GET WELL SOON."

AND ON THE INSIDE IT SAYS, "BECAUSE MY BED ISN'T MADE, MY CLOTHES NEED TO BE PUT AWAY, AND I'M HUNGRY."

"LOVE, CALVIN." WANT TO SIGN IT?

SURE. I'M HUNGRY TOO.

HI, MOM! SINCE YOU'RE SICK, I'M BRINGING YOU BREAKFAST IN BED!

I PREPARED EGGS, TOAST AND ORANGE JUICE FOR YOU ALL BY MYSELF!

HOW NICE!

THE EGGS KIND OF BURNED AND STUCK TO THE PAN, BUT YOU CAN PROBABLY CHIP THEM OUT WITH THIS CHISEL.

UM... WHERE IS THE TOAST AND ORANGE JUICE?

DAD SAID NOT TO TELL YOU ABOUT THAT TILL YOU'RE BETTER.

I ASKED DAD IF MOM WAS GOING TO HAVE A BABY, AND HE SAID NOT THAT *HE* KNEW OF.

DAD SAID WE'D KNOW IF MOM WAS HAVING A KID BECAUSE SHE'D LOOK LIKE A HIPPOPOTAMUS WITH A GLAND PROBLEM.

...THAT'S WHEN MOM CREAMED HIM WITH HER PILLOW.

DAD SAYS SHE MUST BE FEELING BETTER.

YOU HAVE WEIRD PARENTS.

HEY, MOM, I GOT A PART IN THE CLASS PLAY!

I GET TO SAY A LINE, AND EVERYTHING!

THAT'S WONDERFUL, CALVIN.

IT'S A GREAT DRAMATIC ROLE! MY CHARACTER WILL HAVE EVERYONE IN TEARS AT THE END OF THE SECOND ACT!

WHAT'S THE PLAY?

"NUTRITION AND THE FOUR FOOD GROUPS." I'M AN ONION.

OK, HOBBES, I NEED YOU TO HELP ME MEMORIZE MY LINE FOR THE PLAY.

SURE.

I'M THE ONION, AND I SAY, "IN ADDITION TO SUPPLYING VITAL NUTRIENTS, MANY VEGETABLES ARE A SOURCE OF DIETARY FIBER."

OK, READY?

READY. GO AHEAD. "IN ADDITION..."

WAIT. HOLD IT. I'M NOT IN CHARACTER YET. WHAT MOTIVATES AN ONION?

FAME, I SUPPOSE. THIS COULD BE A BIG BREAK.

OK, YOU BE "BREAD." PROMPT ME.

"GLUCOSE IS THE BODY'S MAIN ENERGY SOURCE!"

"IN ADDITION..." UH... UM... "IN ADDITION.." UM...WAIT..

GRRRGHH! I HATE THIS PLAY! I'LL NEVER BE ABLE TO LEARN THIS STUPID PART!

WELL, YOUR EMOTING IS DOWN PAT.

I'VE GOT IT ALL FIGURED OUT, HOBBES. THIS PLAY WILL BE NO SWEAT.

YOU HAVE YOUR LINE ALL MEMORIZED?

NO, I THOUGHT I'D COME OUT, DO A LITTLE SOFT-SHOE, AND AD-LIB SOMETHING!

AD-LIB SOMETHING ABOUT DIETARY FIBER?

EITHER THAT, OR I'LL DO MY ONION IN MIME!

HOW'S MY ONION COSTUME COMING, MOM?

I'M STILL WORKING ON IT. I WISH YOUR CLASS WOULD DO SOMETHING A LITTLE LESS ELABORATE. I'M NOT MUCH OF A SEAMSTRESS.

JUST BE GLAD I'M NOT RUSSY WHITE. *HE* HAS TO BE AN AMINO ACID.

MM... WHAT DO YOU THINK?

JABBA THE HUTT MEETS RUDOLF THE REINDEER. I DUNNO, MOM.

ARE YOU GOING TO COME TO MY PLAY, DAD? IT'S CALLED "NUTRITION AND THE FOUR FOOD GROUPS."

I'LL PROBABLY HAVE TO BE AT WORK, CALVIN.

BUT DAD, IT'LL BE GREAT DRAMA! I'M AN ONION!

WELL, WHY DON'T YOU SAY YOUR LINE FOR ME NOW?

OK! UM... ..LET'S SEE.. "IN ADDITION TO..".. UH... HOLD IT.. UM..

25 KIDS IN FOOD SUITS, FORGETTING THEIR LINES. I'LL DEFINITELY BE AT WORK.

DEAR! CALVIN'S WORKED HARD.

OK, UH... " IN ADDITION.."..UH NO, WAIT.. UM...

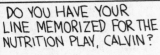

DO YOU HAVE YOUR LINE MEMORIZED FOR THE NUTRITION PLAY, CALVIN?

I'M STILL LEARNING IT. BEING AN ONION IS A DIFFICULT ROLE, YOU KNOW. WHAT ARE YOU?

I'M "FAT."

NO, I MEAN IN THE PLAY.

ANYONE ELSE WANT TO SAY IT ?!?

AACKK! UNDERSTUDY! UNDERSTUDY!

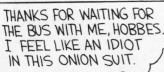

THANKS FOR WAITING FOR THE BUS WITH ME, HOBBES. I FEEL LIKE AN IDIOT IN THIS ONION SUIT.

I'LL BE GLAD WHEN THIS STUPID PLAY IS OVER.

OH NO! RUN FOR YOUR LIFE! A PRODUCE TRUCK!

...JUST KIDDING!

43

44

Calvin and HObbEs by WATTERSON

OP ZIP ZOP ZIP ZOP ZIP ZOP ZIP ZOP ZIP ZOP ZIP ZOP

47

HOW DO THEY KNOW THE LOAD LIMIT ON BRIDGES, DAD?

LOAD LIMIT 10 TONS

THEY DRIVE BIGGER AND BIGGER TRUCKS OVER THE BRIDGE UNTIL IT BREAKS.

THEN THEY WEIGH THE LAST TRUCK AND REBUILD THE BRIDGE.

OH. I SHOULD'VE GUESSED.

DEAR, IF YOU DON'T KNOW THE ANSWER, JUST TELL HIM!

IT'S HARD TO BELIEVE PEOPLE STILL STARVE IN THIS WORLD.

THERE'S EVEN HUNGER IN AMERICA.

SOME PEOPLE NEVER GET ENOUGH TO EAT.

BOY, I KNOW WHAT *THAT'S* LIKE!

NO YOU DON'T.

THE SOLDIERS ADVANCE UP THE HILL!

OH, NO! A SQUADRON OF BOMBERS APPEARS ON THE HORIZON! THE BOMBS BEGIN TO FALL!

BONK BONK

TWO DIRECT HITS!

I SEE YOU UP THERE!

50

I CAN'T BELIEVE OUR BABY SITTER PUT US TO BED! IT'S NOT EVEN DARK OUT!

WELL, SHE CAN PUT US TO BED, BUT SHE CAN'T MAKE US SLEEP. YOU PLAY THE HORN, AND I'LL ACCOMPANY ON TOM-TOM.

CALVIN, I JUST WANTED TO REMIND YOU THAT SLEEPING IN A BED IS A *PRIVILEGE*. THE BASEMENT IS SURE TO BE A LOT LESS COMFY.

WHAT DID SHE MEAN, "THE BASEMENT"?

SHHH!

ROSALYN, WE'RE GOING TO BE A LITTLE LATER THAN WE EXPECTED, SO I THOUGHT I'D BETTER CALL YOU.

THAT'S FINE. CALVIN WENT TO BED EARLY, SO I'M JUST HOLDING DOWN THE FORT.

WHO'S ON THE PHONE? IS IT MY MOM? I WANT TO TALK TO HER! MOM! MOM! CAN YOU HEAR ME?!

COME HOME NOW BEFORE IT'S TOO LATE! HELP! HELP!

NO, THAT'S JUST THE TV. I'LL SEE YOU AT 11:30 THEN. ENJOY THE PLAY.

SORRY WE'RE LATE, ROSALYN. DID YOU GET CALVIN TO BED?

YES, BUT...

MOM! DAD! IS THAT YOU? I'M NOT ASLEEP! DID YOU GET RID OF THE BABY SITTER? THANK GOODNESS YOU'RE HOME!

HAS HE BEEN THIS WAY ALL NIGHT?

WELL, HIS VOICE GAVE OUT ABOUT 11 O'CLOCK, BUT IT SEEMS TO BE...

IF SHE'S STILL HERE, DON'T PAY HER!

GIVE HER A LITTLE EXTRA, WILL YOU, DEAR?

IS FIVE ENOUGH?

COULD YOU MAKE IT EIGHT? COLLEGE TUITIONS ARE UP.

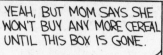

BAD NEWS ON YOUR POLLS, DAD.

YOU SLIPPED ANOTHER TWO NOTCHES. THINGS ARE LOOKING GRIM FOR FUTURE OFFICE.

IS THAT SO?

ANY IDEAS ON WHAT WOULD IMPROVE MY STANDINGS?

I NEED A VCR.

RIGHT. I'LL KEEP THAT IN MIND.

I HOPE YOU'RE READING THE "HELP WANTED" SECTION.

LOOK, I GOT A LETTER I'M SUPPOSED TO COPY AND SEND TO 20 PEOPLE FOR GOOD LUCK.

IT'S A CHAIN LETTER.

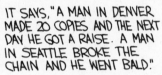
IT SAYS, "A MAN IN DENVER MADE 20 COPIES AND THE NEXT DAY HE GOT A RAISE. A MAN IN SEATTLE BROKE THE CHAIN AND HE WENT BALD!"

HA! YOU BELIEVE THAT? THESE LETTERS ARE FOR SUPERSTITIOUS NINCOMPOOPS. THROW IT AWAY.

"...AND A DUMB KID LIKE YOU LISTENED TO A FRIEND AND GOT RUN OVER BY A CEMENT MIXER."

CALVIN HAS MYSTERIOUSLY SHRUNK TO THE SIZE OF AN INSECT!

HIS ONLY HOPE IS TO CALL FOR HELP! PUSHING WITH ALL HIS MIGHT, CALVIN DIALS THE GIGANTIC TELEPHONE!

IT'S RINGING! HE RUNS TO THE MOUTHPIECE! WILL ANYONE BE ABLE TO HEAR HIM??

BZZ BZ! BZZZZ! BZZ BZZ! BZZZ BZ!

CALVIN, THIS HAD BETTER NOT BE YOU.

55

Calvin and Hobbes

by WATTERSON

I'M READY FOR BED, DAD. WHAT'S TONIGHT'S STORY GOING TO BE?

HERE'S ONE. "READINGS ON DIALECTICAL METAPHYSICS." YOU'LL LOVE IT.

FORGET IT, DAD. YOU CAN'T GET ME TO DROP OFF *THAT* EASY.

WILL YOU READ US *THIS* STORY? HOBBES WROTE IT HIMSELF.

HOBBES WROTE IT, HUH?

"GOLDILOCKS AND THE THREE TIGERS."

OH BOY, THIS IS GONNA BE GREAT!

"ONCE UPON A TIME THERE LIVED A YOUNG GIRL NAMED GOLDILOCKS. SHE WENT INTO THE FOREST AND SAW A COTTAGE. NO ONE WAS HOME SO SHE WENT IN."

"INSIDE SHE SAW THREE BOWLS OF PORRIDGE. A BIG BOWL, A MEDIUM BOWL, AND A SMALL BOWL. SHE WAS JUST ABOUT TO TASTE THE PORRIDGE WHEN THE THREE TIGERS CAME HOME."

"THEY QUICKLY DIVIDED GOLDILOCKS INTO BIG, MEDIUM, AND SMALL PIECES AND DUNKED THEM IN THE PORRIDGE THAT..."

CALVIN, I'M NOT GOING TO FINISH THIS! THIS IS DISGUSTING!!

I DON'T KNOW WHY I LET YOU TALK ME INTO THIS. *GOOD NIGHT!*

CLICK

HE DIDN'T EVEN LOOK AT OUR ILLUSTRATIONS.

NOW I'M ALL HUNGRY.

FWOOSHHH

WATTERSON

GREETINGS, EARTH FEMALE. DO NOT BE ALARMED.

OUR PLANET IS DYING. WE NEED COOKIES TO SURVIVE. DO NOT TRY TO RESIST OR YOU WILL BE DESTROYED.

WE'LL SEE ABOUT THAT. GET BACK HERE.

WHY DO I HAVE TO GO TO BED NOW? I NEVER GET TO DO WHAT I WANT!

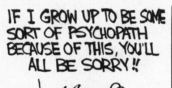

IF I GROW UP TO BE SOME SORT OF PSYCHOPATH BECAUSE OF THIS, YOU'LL ALL BE SORRY!!

WATTERSON

NOBODY EVER BECAME A PSYCHOPATH BECAUSE HE HAD TO GO TO BED AT A REASONABLE HOUR.

YEAH, BUT YOU WON'T LET ME CHEW TOBACCO EITHER! YOU NEVER KNOW WHAT MIGHT PUSH ME OVER THE BRINK!

GO TO BED, CALVIN.

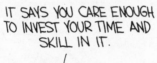

PSST! ARE YOU AWAKE?

IS IT CHRISTMAS? IT IS! IT IS!

LET'S GO WAKE MOM AND DAD AND OPEN ALL OUR LOOT!

SINCE IT'S CHRISTMAS, MAYBE WE SHOULD LET THEM SLEEP IN A LITTLE.

THAT'S LONG ENOUGH! WAKE UP! WAKE UP! IT'S CHRISTMAS!!

QUARTER TO 6. HE LET US SLEEP IN THIS YEAR.

OMIGOSH! THIS LIBRARY BOOK WAS DUE TWO DAYS AGO!

WHAT WILL THEY *DO*? ARE THEY GOING TO INTERROGATE ME AND BEAT ME UP?! ARE THEY GOING TO BREAK MY KNEES?? WILL I HAVE TO SIGN SOME CONFESSION???

THEY'LL FINE YOU TEN CENTS. NOW GO RETURN IT.

THE WAY SOME OF THOSE LIBRARIANS LOOK AT YOU, I NATURALLY ASSUMED THE CONSEQUENCES WOULD BE MORE DIRE.

HEY DAD, I HAVE A QUESTION.

SURE, CALVIN. WHAT DO YOU WANT TO KNOW?

IF YOU PLUGGED UP YOUR NOSE AND MOUTH RIGHT BEFORE YOU SNEEZED...

...WOULD THE SNEEZE GO OUT YOUR EARS, OR WOULD YOUR HEAD EXPLODE?

I WAS KIND OF HOPING YOU HAD A MATH PROBLEM OR SOMETHING.

...EITHER WAY, I'M SCARED TO TRY IT.

CALVIN and HOBBES

by WATTERSON

RUN! AIEEE! LOOK OUT!

I WONDER WHY JAPANESE PEOPLE KEEP MOVING THEIR MOUTHS AFTER THEY'RE THROUGH TALKING.

SOMEWHERE IN THE PACIFIC OCEAN...

AN UNDERSEA NUCLEAR EXPLOSION AWAKENS A GIANT PREHISTORIC MONSTER!

IT MAKES ITS WAY TO THE COAST OF JAPAN AND EMERGES!

YAARGHHH

HE HEADS FOR THE POWER LINES, LEAVING A TRAIL OF DESTRUCTION BEHIND!

CALVIN, GET BACK IN THE TUB! YOU'RE MAKING A MESS!

HIS ANCIENT ARCH-RIVAL MEGALON!

HE SPEWS A MIGHTY FIREBALL!

AAUUGHH

TOKYO IS IN RUINS! MEGALON VANQUISHED! HE RETURNS TO THE SEA FROM WHENCE HE CAME!

NO MORE AFTERNOON TV MOVIES FOR YOU! ...EVER!!

CALVIN, I HOPE YOU TOOK YOUR BOOTS OFF BEFORE YOU WALKED ACROSS THE FLOOR.

OF COURSE I DID! YOU DON'T NEED TO TELL ME ALL THE TIME!

WATTERSON

GIVEN ANY MORE THOUGHT TO THAT BACKYARD SKI LIFT PROPOSAL OF MINE?

OH, YES. LOTS.

WATTERSON

HOBBES IS ALWAYS A LITTLE LOOPY WHEN HE COMES OUT OF THE DRYER.

WATTERSON

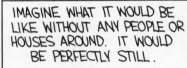

WHIFFFFFF... o

WHIFF
WHIFF
WHIFF
WHIFF
WHIFF

FOR ALL THAT PREPARATION, YOU SURE ARE A LOUSY SHOT!

GO AHEAD DOWN. YOU'LL MISS ALL THOSE TREES.

YOU CAN DO IT. YOU'LL STOP BEFORE YOU GO OVER THAT LEDGE AT THE BOTTOM.

YOU WON'T GO INTO THAT POND. BESIDES, THE ICE IS PROBABLY REAL THICK ANYWAY. GO AHEAD DOWN.

MY BRAIN IS TRYING TO KILL ME.

GALOSH
GALOSH
GALOSH

I CALLED SUSIE A BOOGER-BRAIN AFTER SCHOOL, AND SHE WENT HOME CRYING.

GOODNESS, WHY'D YOU DO *THAT*?

I DUNNO. I WAS JUST TEASING.

IT SOUNDS LIKE YOU HURT HER FEELINGS.

I DIDN'T MEAN FOR HER TO TAKE THE INSULT *PERSONALLY!*

WATTERSON

＊SNIFF＊ THAT STUPID CALVIN. WHY DOES HE CALL ME NAMES FOR NO REASON? IT'S JUST MEAN.

I WISH I HAD A HUNDRED FRIENDS. *THEN* I WOULDN'T CARE. I'D SAY, "WHO NEEDS *YOU*, CALVIN? I'VE GOT A HUNDRED OTHER FRIENDS!"

THEN MY HUNDRED FRIENDS AND I WOULD GO DO SOMETHING FUN, AND LEAVE CALVIN ALL ALONE! HA!

...AND AS LONG AS I'M DREAMING, I'D LIKE A PONY.

I FEEL BAD THAT I CALLED SUSIE NAMES AND HURT HER FEELINGS.

I'M SORRY I DID IT.

MAYBE YOU SHOULD APOLOGIZE TO HER.

I KEEP HOPING THERE'S A LESS OBVIOUS SOLUTION.

WATTERSON

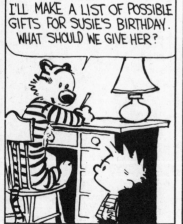

74

HERE'S A PAPER PLATE FOR THE BIRTHDAY CAKE, CALVIN.

THANK YOU.

I HOPE IT'S GOOD. I HATE IT WHEN THE BIRTHDAY KID CHOOSES SOMETHING GROSS LIKE COCONUT.

YOU DON'T HAVE TO WORRY. IT'S CHOCOLATE.

OH, GOOD. DID YOU SEE IT?

HEY! WHO CUT A PIECE OF MY CAKE ALREADY?! I DIDN'T EVEN GET TO BLOW OUT THE CANDLES!!

IT'S NICE AND MOIST, TOO.

GLAD YOU BOTH COULD COME. THANK YOU FOR THE NICE PRESENT. GOOD-BYE.

MOM MAY NOT WANT THIS PIECE OF CAKE AND ICE CREAM WE'RE BRINGING HER.

HEY! IT SNOWED LAST NIGHT!

OH, BOY! LOOK AT IT ALL! THEY'LL HAVE TO CLOSE THE SCHOOLS!

SNOW EVERYWHERE! IT MUST BE WAIST DEEP!

UNFORTUNATELY, THAT'S A RELATIVE MEASURE.

76

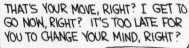

Calvin and Hobbes

by WATTERSON

WHY CAN'T I EVER FIND MY STUPID SCARF?

HOBBES AND I ARE GOING OUTSIDE, MOM.

THIS IS GOING TO BE THE BIGGEST SNOWMAN EVER BUILT!

PEOPLE WILL COME FROM MILES TO SEE OUR GIGANTIC SNOWMAN!

THIS WON'T GO ANY MORE. IT'S TOO BIG TO PUSH.

OK, LEAVE IT HERE.

I'M EXHAUSTED!

WELL WE CAN'T STOP NOW! WE NEED NINE MORE OF THESE!

NINE MORE?!

SURE! THIS IS JUST ONE OF HIS TOES!

WATTERSON

Calvin and Hobbes
by WATTERSON

HERE IS SUCCESSFUL MR. JONES. HE LIVES IN A 5-ACRE HOME IN A WEALTHY SUBURB. HERE IS HIS NEW MERCEDES IN THE DRIVEWAY.

IT'S ANYONE'S GUESS AS TO HOW MUCH LONGER MR. JONES CAN MEET HIS MONTHLY FINANCE CHARGES.

HERE COMES MR. JONES OUT OF HIS ATTRACTIVE SUBURBAN HOME. HE HOPS IN HIS RED SPORTS CAR.

OFF HE GOES TO WORK. 80 ... 90 ... 100 MILES AN HOUR!

...ALONG THE EDGE OF THE GRAND CANYON !!

SUDDENLY, HIS STEERING LOCKS AND HIS BRAKES FAIL! HE CAREENS OVER THE EDGE! OH NO! DOWN HE GOES!

HIS ONLY HOPE IS TO CLIMB OUT THE SUN ROOF AND JUMP! MAYBE, JUST MAYBE, HE CAN GRAB A BRANCH AND SAVE HIMSELF! HE UNWINDS THE SUN ROOF! CAN HE MAKE IT ??

NO! THE CAR EXPLODES IN MID-AIR, PROPELLING MILLIONS OF TINY SHARDS INTO THE STRATOSPHERE! *KABLOOIE!*

THE NEIGHBORS HEAR THE BOOM ECHOING ACROSS THE CANYON. THEY PILE INTO A MINI-VAN TO INVESTIGATE! WHAT WILL HAPPEN TO *THEM*?

THE MAJESTIC EAGLE CIRCLES SLOWLY IN THE CLOUDS.

WITH EYES SO SHARP HE CAN SPOT MOVEMENT A MILE BELOW, HE SIGHTS HIS PREY AND DIVES!

REACHING SPEEDS OF MORE THAN 100 MPH, HIS UNWARY PRIZE WILL NEVER KNOW WHAT HIT IT!

WAKE UP, DAD! IT'S SATURDAY!

ZZ... WHA?

DAD, DID YOU DO A MATING DANCE WHEN YOU FIRST SAW MOM?

A MATING DANCE?

YEAH. I SAW SOME BIRDS DO IT ON TV.

THEY WENT, "AWK AWK BRAAU-AUUKKK!"

YES, THAT'S MORE OR LESS HOW I REACTED.

TO WHAT, WISE GUY? ...THINK CAREFULLY.

OUT YOU GO, HOBBES. INTO THE DRYER.

RRRRRR

DING!

GOODNESS, YOU'RE A FRIGHT.

TELL YOUR MOM TO PUT SOME CONDITIONER IN THE WASH NEXT TIME.

Calvin and Hobbes by WATTERSON

AAAAAHHH! EEEE! HEE HEE HEE HEE! WOO! ACK! HEE

OH, MOM, I NEED SOME CRISCO FOR SCHOOL TODAY!

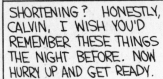

SHORTENING? HONESTLY, CALVIN, I WISH YOU'D REMEMBER THESE THINGS THE NIGHT BEFORE. NOW HURRY UP AND GET READY.

RIGHT.

HERE'S THE CRISCO BACK. THANKS.

YOU PUT IT IN YOUR HAIR??

GET BACK HERE! YOU'RE NOT GOING TO SCHOOL LIKE THAT!

AW C'MON, MOM! IT'S CLASS PICTURE DAY!

WHAT'S WITH YOUR HAIR?

I TOLD MOM I'M GETTING MY SCHOOL PICTURE TAKEN TODAY, AND SHE MADE ME COMB OUT THE CRISCO I PUT IN MY HAIR. NOW I LOOK LIKE A MORON.

THAT'S TRUE. YOU DO.

WELL DON'T JUST STAND THERE! THINK OF SOMETHING! WHAT CAN I DO?

THERE. MUCH BETTER!

WHAT'D YOU DO? IS IT COOL? IS IT NEW WAVE? GEE, I WISH I HAD A MIRROR...

THE BUS IS GOING TO BE HERE ANY MINUTE. YOU'RE SURE YOU FIXED MY HAIR SO IT LOOKS OK?

IT LOOKS GREAT. TRY NOT TO MUSS IT UP.

YOU'RE NOT KIDDING ME, ARE YOU? THIS REALLY LOOKS GOOD?

TRUST ME. YOU LOOK LIKE ... LIKE...

"...ASTRO BOY."

ALL RIGHT! I CAN'T WAIT TO GET MY PICTURE TAKEN NOW!

CALVIN! WHAT DID YOU DO TO YOUR HAIR ?? DON'T YOU KNOW WE HAVE OUR PICTURES TAKEN TODAY?

OF COURSE, SILLY. THAT'S WHY I DID IT. IT'S CRISCO.

DOES YOUR MOM KNOW YOU LOOK LIKE THAT?

SORT OF. HOBBES FIXED ME UP A LITTLE AT THE BUS STOP.

WOW. I WISH *I* HAD SOME CRISCO.

WAIT TILL MOM SENDS MY PICTURE TO GRANDMA!

OK, KID, SIT UP STRAIGHT ON THE STOOL AND LOOK RIGHT AT ME. THAT'S IT.

ARE YOU READY TO TAKE MY PICTURE? SHOULD I TAKE OFF MY SHIRT NOW?

KID, WHAT ARE...? DON'T TAKE OFF YOUR SHIRT !!

SEE? I PAINTED A FACE ON MY STOMACH.

KID, PUT YOUR SHIRT BACK ON.

BUT LOOK! WHEN I BREATHE OUT, THE FACE CHANGES! SEE? OK, TAKE ONE QUICK!

LOOK, HOBBES, I GOT MY SCHOOL PICTURES BACK.

LOOK AT YOU! HA HA HA! LOOK AT YOUR HAIR! HEE HEE! THESE ARE GREAT!

AREN'T THEY, THOUGH?

HEE HEE HEE! LOOK AT THIS ONE! WHAT AN EXPRESSION! HOO HOO HOO! HA HA!

YEAH, SEE HOW I GOT MY ONE EYE TO ROLL BACK ?

HA HA HA! YOUR MOTHER'S GOING TO GO INTO CONNIPTIONS, OF COURSE...

OH, C'MON. YEARS FROM NOW, THINK OF THE MEMORIES THESE WILL BRING.

Calvin and Hobbes

by WATTERSON

GLIK
GLIK
GLIK

OH NO! WHAT HAVE I DONE?!?

THE HUMAN BODY IS 80% WATER. LITTLE DID CALVIN REALIZE HOW CRITICAL IT IS TO MAINTAIN THAT!

NOW IT'S TOO LATE! BY DRINKING THAT EXTRA GLASS OF WATER, CALVIN HAS UPSET THAT PRECIOUS BALANCE! HE IS NOW **90%** WATER!

EVERYTHING SOLID IN CALVIN'S BODY BEGINS TO DISSOLVE!

HE IS BECOMING A LIQUID!!

HIS ONLY HOPE IS SOMEHOW TO GET TO AN ICEBOX AND FREEZE HIMSELF SOLID UNTIL HE CAN GET PROPER MEDICAL ATTENTION!

UNFORTUNATELY, AS A LIQUID, CALVIN CAN ONLY RUN DOWNHILL! CAN HE MAKE IT? CAN HE MAKE IT??

I DON'T THINK I'M GONNA MAKE IT.

THERE'S A GAS STATION UP AHEAD. JUST HOLD ON.

DIDN'T I TELL YOU NOT TO DRINK SO MUCH BEFORE WE LEFT?!

HOBBES, LOOK! THERE'S A LITTLE RACCOON ON THE GROUND.

IS IT ALIVE?

I THINK SO, BUT HE'S HURT. SEE, HE'S HARDLY BREATHING.

BETTER NOT TOUCH HIM IF HE'S HURT.

YEAH. YOU WAIT HERE AND GUARD HIM. I'LL RUN AND GET MOM.

I SURE HOPE SHE CAN HELP.

OF COURSE SHE CAN! YOU DON'T GET TO BE MOM IF YOU CAN'T FIX EVERYTHING JUST RIGHT.

WATTERSON

THERE'S HOBBES GUARDING HIM, MOM. THE LITTLE RACCOON'S RIGHT OVER THERE!

OOH, CALVIN, I DON'T KNOW IF WE CAN SAVE HIM. HE LOOKS PRETTY BAD. GO GET A SHOE BOX AND A CLEAN DISH TOWEL.

RIGHT!

I DON'T THINK THIS POOR LITTLE GUY IS GOING TO MAKE IT, HOBBES. (SIGH) I HATE IT WHEN THESE THINGS HAPPEN.

WATTERSON

...YOU CAN TELL I'M UPSET WHEN I START TALKING TO YOU...

WELL, I GOT HIM IN THE SHOE BOX. I GUESS ALL WE CAN DO IS KEEP HIM WARM AND SAFE.

WE'LL KEEP HIM IN THE GARAGE, AND PUT OUT SOME WATER AND FOOD.

I READ IN A BOOK THAT RACCOONS WILL EAT JUST ABOUT ANYTHING.

WATTERSON

CHANCES ARE, I'LL BE HAPPY TO DONATE MOST OF MY DINNER.

CALVIN, YOU DON'T EVEN KNOW WHAT WE'RE HAVING.

THIS IS WHERE DAD BURIED THE LITTLE RACCOON.

I DIDN'T EVEN KNOW HE EXISTED A FEW DAYS AGO AND NOW HE'S GONE FOREVER. IT'S LIKE I FOUND HIM FOR NO REASON. I HAD TO SAY GOOD-BYE AS SOON AS I SAID HELLO.

STILL... IN A SAD, AWFUL, TERRIBLE WAY, I'M HAPPY I MET HIM.

SNIFF

WHAT A STUPID WORLD.

WATTERSON

YOU KNOW, HOBBES, I CAN'T FIGURE OUT THIS DEATH STUFF.

WHY DID THAT LITTLE RACCOON HAVE TO DIE? HE DIDN'T DO ANYTHING WRONG.

HE WAS JUST LITTLE! WHAT'S THE POINT OF PUTTING HIM HERE AND TAKING HIM BACK SO SOON ?!?

IT'S EITHER MEAN OR IT'S ARBITRARY, AND EITHER WAY I'VE GOT THE HEEBIE-JEEBIES.

WHY IS IT ALWAYS NIGHT WHEN WE TALK ABOUT THESE THINGS

WATTERSON

MOM SAYS DEATH IS AS NATURAL AS BIRTH, AND IT'S ALL PART OF THE LIFE CYCLE.

SHE SAYS WE DON'T REALLY UNDERSTAND IT, BUT THERE ARE MANY THINGS WE DON'T UNDERSTAND, AND WE JUST HAVE TO DO THE BEST WE CAN WITH THE KNOWLEDGE WE HAVE.

I GUESS THAT MAKES SENSE.

...BUT DON'T *YOU* GO ANYWHERE.

DON'T WORRY.

WATTERSON

HEY! WHAT HAPPENED TO THE TREES HERE? WHO CLEARED OUT THE WOODS?

THERE USED TO BE LOTS OF ANIMALS IN THESE WOODS! NOW IT'S A MUD PIT!

THIS SIGN SAYS, "FUTURE SITE OF SHADY ACRES CONDOMINIUMS."

ANIMALS CAN'T AFFORD CONDOS!

"SHADY ACRES"? THE ONLY SHADE *I* SEE IS FROM THAT BULLDOZER.

WHERE ARE ALL THE ANIMALS SUPPOSED TO LIVE NOW THAT THEY CUT DOWN THESE WOODS TO PUT IN HOUSES??

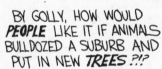

BY GOLLY, HOW WOULD *PEOPLE* LIKE IT IF ANIMALS BULLDOZED A SUBURB AND PUT IN NEW *TREES*?!?

NO GOOD. THEY DIDN'T LEAVE THE KEYS.

IT TOOK HUNDREDS OF YEARS FOR THESE WOODS TO GROW, AND THEY LEVELED IT IN A WEEK. IT'S GONE.

AFTER THEY BUILD NEW HOUSES HERE, THEY'LL HAVE TO WIDEN THE ROADS AND PUT UP GAS STATIONS, AND PRETTY SOON THIS WHOLE AREA WILL JUST BE A BIG STRIP.

EVENTUALLY THERE WON'T BE A NICE SPOT LEFT ANYWHERE.

I WONDER IF YOU CAN REFUSE TO INHERIT THE WORLD.

I THINK IF YOU'RE BORN, IT'S TOO LATE.

Calvin and Hobbes

KABLOOIE!

OOOOH, YOU'VE TWICKED ME FOR THE WAST TIME, WABBIT!

HA HA HA! BOY, I WISH *I* HAD SOME DYNAMITE!

BOY, I LOVE WEEKENDS! WHAT BETTER WAY TO SPEND ONE'S FREEDOM THAN EATING CHOCOLATE CEREAL AND WATCHING CARTOONS!

MM... I BEG TO DIFFER ON THE CEREAL PART.

CALVIN, YOU'VE BEEN SITTING IN FRONT OF THAT STUPID TV ALL MORNING! IT'S A BEAUTIFUL DAY! YOU SHOULD BE OUTSIDE!

IT'S GOING TO BE A GRIM DAY WHEN THE WORLD IS RUN BY A GENERATION THAT DOESN'T KNOW ANYTHING BUT WHAT IT'S SEEN ON TV!

click

HEY!

HOW CAN YOU SIT INSIDE ALL DAY? GO ON! OUT! OUT!

KIDS ARE SUPPOSED TO RUN AROUND IN THE FRESH AIR! HAVE SOME FUN! GET SOME EXERCISE!

SLAM!

WELL, I GUESS THAT'S THAT. COME ON.

HI, SUSIE, ARE YOU WATCHING TV? CAN WE COME IN?

SURE, HURRY UP! IT'S A COMMERCIAL.

101

Calvin and Hobbes

by WATTERSON

THANKS FOR THE LUNCH, MOM! I'M GOING OUTSIDE.

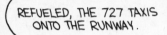

REFUELED, THE 727 TAXIS ONTO THE RUNWAY.

CONTROL TOWER TO CALVIN, YOU ARE CLEARED FOR TAKE OFF.

ROGER.

FULL THROTTLE! FWOOOSHH!

TAKE OFF! LANDING GEAR UP! CHUGUNK!

WE HAVE REACHED OUR CRUISING ALTITUDE OF 30,000 FEET. A SMALL, TASTELESS SNACK WILL BE SERVED SHORTLY.

THIS IS YOUR CAPTAIN SPEAKING. I'M AFRAID OUR ARRIVAL WILL BE SLIGHTLY DELAYED.

WE'RE STACKED UP OVER WASHINGTON, AND WE'LL BE IN A HOLDING PATTERN FOR ANOTHER 40 MINUTES.

TOWER TO CALVIN, YOU ARE NOW CLEARED FOR LANDING.

ROGER. LANDING GEAR DOWN! REVERSE THRUST!

WATTERSON

I SAW YOU OUTSIDE RUNNING IN CIRCLES FOR ALMOST AN HOUR! ARE YOU TRYING TO MAKE YOURSELF SICK?!?

OOG, FROM NOW ON, I'M PLAYING "BUS."

Calvin and Hobbes

by WATTERSON

Look, Jane. See Spot.
See Spot run.
Run, Spot, run.
Jane sees Spot run.

106

RRINNGGG!

RECESS IS OVER!

R-R-RIPP!

SNAG

OH NO!

WHY IS IT YOU ALWAYS RIP YOUR PANTS ON THE DAY EVERYONE HAS TO DEMONSTRATE A MATH PROBLEM AT THE CHALKBOARD?

I CAN'T BELIEVE I RIPPED MY PANTS! RECESS IS OVER. I'M SUPPOSED TO BE BACK IN CLASS!

I CAN'T GO IN LIKE THIS! WHAT AM I GOING TO DO??

...OF ALL THE DAYS TO WEAR THE UNDERPANTS WITH THE LITTLE ROCKET SHIPS...

LOOK AT THE SIZE OF THIS RIP! MAYBE I CAN PULL MY SHIRT DOWN OVER IT.

NO, THAT DOESN'T WORK. MAYBE I CAN TUCK MY SHIRT INTO THE HOLE. ..NOPE..

MAYBE I CAN STICK THE RIPPED PART UNDER MY BELT. NO, THAT DOESN'T WORK EITHER.

MAYBE I CAN SCOOT AROUND ON MY REAR THE REST OF THE DAY.

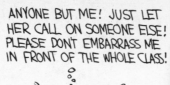

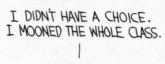

CALVIN and HOBBES

"DURING EMERGENCY LANDING, REPLACE DINNER TRAY AND BRING SEAT TO UPRIGHT POSITION. EXTINGUISH ALL SMOKING MATERIALS."

"...INCLUDING SPACECRAFT, IF POSSIBLE."

OUT OF FUEL, THE COURAGEOUS SPACEMAN SPIFF IS FORCED TO LAND ON THE DISTANT PLANET ZOK!

THE VALIANT EXPLORER SURVEYS THE ZOKKIAN LANDSCAPE. WHO KNOWS WHAT DANGERS LIE HIDDEN IN THE CRATERED TERRAIN?

UNDAUNTED, SPIFF SETS OUT TO FIND HELP!

MILES LATER, IT IS EVIDENT THE PLANET IS COMPLETELY UNINHABITED!

OUR HERO IS MAROONED ON A LIFELESS PLANET! ALONE ON AN ALIEN WORLD!

ALONE... ALL ALONE...

DARN IT, WHY DOESN'T ANYONE EVER *TELL* ME WHEN THE LUNCH BELL RINGS?

WATTERSON

109

SUSIE, WHERE'S MISS WORMWOOD? WHO'S THAT LADY AT HER DESK?

MISS WORMWOOD'S SICK. THAT'S OUR SUBSTITUTE TEACHER.

A SUBSTITUTE?

LET'S SEE YOUR TEACHING CERTIFICATE, LADY!

GOOD MORNING, CLASS. I'LL BE YOUR SUBSTITUTE TEACHER TODAY.

MISS WORMWOOD LEFT ME INSTRUCTIONS AS TO WHAT WE NEED TO GO OVER, SO WE SHOULDN'T HAVE ANY PROBLEMS.

OH WAIT, HERE'S A NOTE SHE ADDED. JUST A SECOND...

OK, WHICH ONE OF YOU IS CALVIN?

NOT ME!

WE HAD A SUBSTITUTE TEACHER IN SCHOOL TODAY.

DID YOU LIKE HER?

SHE WAS OK, I GUESS.

YOU "GUESS"?

IT'S HARD TO SAY.

SHE WENT HOME AT NOON.

Mr. Jones lives 50 miles away from you. You both leave home at 5:00 and drive toward each other.

Mr. Jones travels at 35 mph., and you drive at 40 mph. At what time will you pass Mr. Jones on the road?

GIVEN THE TRAFFIC AROUND HERE at 5:00, WHO KNOWS?

I ALWAYS CATCH THESE TRICK QUESTIONS.

I'VE GOT A SCHEME TO GET US SOME MONEY.

OH BOY.

SEE? I SNEAKED ALL THESE KERNELS OF CORN OFF MY DINNER PLATE TONIGHT.

HOW IS THAT GOING TO GET US MONEY?

EASY. I JUST STICK THEM UNDER MY PILLOW.

WITH ANY LUCK, THE TOOTH FAIRY WON'T KNOW THEY'RE FAKES UNTIL IT'S TOO LATE!

DAD, HOW DO PEOPLE MAKE BABIES?

MOST PEOPLE JUST GO TO SEARS, BUY THE KIT, AND FOLLOW THE ASSEMBLY INSTRUCTIONS.

I CAME FROM SEARS??

NO, YOU WERE A BLUE LIGHT SPECIAL AT K MART. ALMOST AS GOOD, AND A LOT CHEAPER.

AAUUGHHH!

DEAR, WHAT ARE YOU TELLING CALVIN NOW?!

I'VE GOT TO GIVE A 5-MINUTE ORAL REPORT IN SCHOOL ON THURSDAY.

WE'RE SUPPOSED TO RESEARCH OUR SUBJECT, WRITE IT UP, AND PRESENT IT TO THE CLASS WITH A VISUAL AID.

THAT'S A BIG ASSIGNMENT.

I'LL SAY. I HATE MY TEACHER.

SHE KNOWS WE'LL ALL DO IT ON THE LAST EVENING, BUT SHE GAVE US THREE DAYS TO WORRY ABOUT IT.

WHAT'S THE SUBJECT OF YOUR REPORT?

THE BRAIN.

WHAT DO YOU KNOW ABOUT BRAINS?

WELL, I SAW THIS MOVIE WHERE THEY KEPT THIS GUY'S BRAIN ALIVE IN A TANK OF WATER.

THEN A POWER SURGE MUTATED THE BRAIN, AND IT CRAWLED OUT AND TERRORIZED THE POPULACE.

THAT'S INFORMATIVE.

UNFORTUNATELY FOR MY REPORT, MOM CAUGHT ME, AND I DIDN'T GET TO SEE HOW IT ENDED.

I'VE GOT TO GIVE MY REPORT ON "THE BRAIN" AT SCHOOL TODAY.

SEE MY VISUAL AID? I COOKED SOME NOODLES AND PUT THEM IN A PAPER BAG. DOESN'T THAT LOOK LIKE BRAINS?

UGH.

WELL, I GUESS I'M ALL SET.

DID YOU WRITE YOUR REPORT YET?

NAH. I BORROWED MOM'S POCKET DICTIONARY. I'LL DO IT ON THE BUS.

MY FIVE-MINUTE REPORT IS ON "THE BRAIN."

OF COURSE, IT'S DIFFICULT TO EXPLAIN THE COMPLEXITIES OF THE BRAIN IN JUST FIVE MINUTES, BUT TO BEGIN, THE BRAIN IS PART OF THE CENTRAL NERVOUS SYSTEM.

I'LL PAUSE FOR A FEW MOMENTS, SO YOU ALL CAN FINISH WRITING THAT DOWN.

CALVIN!

POW! JAB! KICK! POW! POW!

RATTATATTATTATTA RATTATATTATTA

EEEEEEEEEEE

BOOM!

PLEASE, PLEASE, PRETTY PLEASE?

NO. YOU SHOULD'VE SAVED SOME OF YOUR OWN HALLOWEEN CANDY.

HEY, CAN WE CHANGE THE CHANNEL NOW? I WANT TO WATCH SOMETHING ELSE.

MY SHOW'S NOT OVER YET.

AW C'MON! YOU SEE THIS PROGRAM ALL THE TIME! CAN'T WE WATCH MY SHOW FOR ONCE?

NO, I WAS HERE FIRST. PIPE DOWN. THIS IS A GOOD PART.

AARRGHH

I HATE NATIONAL GEOGRAPHIC ANIMAL SPECIALS.

Point A is twice as far from point C as point B is from A. If the distance from point B to point C is 5 inches, how far is point A from point C?

THE LIVING DEAD DON'T *NEED* TO SOLVE WORD PROBLEMS.

CALVIN THE ZOMBIE SEARCHES FOR FOOD.

HORRIBLY, THE UNDEAD FEED UPON THE LIVING!

...ALTHOUGH, IN A PINCH, A PBJ WILL DO, IF YOU EAT IT MESSILY ENOUGH.

117

LOOK, I'M SORRY I GAVE YOU A BAD HAIRCUT. I DIDN'T *MEAN* TO.

A FAT LOT OF GOOD *THAT* DOES ME.

I CAN MAKE IT UP TO YOU. HONEST.

YEAH? HOW?

I BOUGHT A YELLOW MAGIC MARKER.

SEE, I'LL JUST *DRAW* SOME HAIR ON. THERE, IT'S LOOKING BETTER ALREADY.

REALLY? IS IT?

WELL, YOUR HAIR DOESN'T STICK UP THE WAY IT USED TO, BUT AT LEAST YOUR HEAD'S YELLOW AGAIN.

THANKS, HOBBES. YOU'RE A REAL LIFE SAVER. I'M SORRY I GOT SO MAD AT YOU.

NONSENSE. NO HARM DONE.

BOY, WAIT TILL I SHOW MOM!

UH OH. DOES IT COME OFF?

FROM NOW ON, JUST KEEP YOUR BRAINY IDEAS TO YOURSELF, OK?

BOOK REPORT "Treasure Island"

calvin and HOBBES
by WATTERSON

THIS IS SUPPOSED TO BE GREAT ART.

...SO WHY DOES IT LOOK LIKE A BUNCH OF DECAPITATED NAKED PEOPLE?

A STRANGE FEELING COMES OVER CALVIN IN THE ART MUSEUM.

HIS PARENTS, ENGROSSED IN CULTURE, REMAIN BLISSFULLY UNAWARE OF CALVIN'S TERRIBLE TRANSFORMATION!

YES, A TYRANNOSAURUS IS LOOSE IN THE ART MUSEUM! THE CURATOR SHRIEKS, AND PANDEMONIUM ENSUES!

A GUARD REACHES FOR HIS PISTOL, BUT THE DINOSAUR IS UPON HIM AND HE IS MESSILY DEVOURED!

THE GIANT LIZARD'S GLORY IS CAP-TURED FOREVER ON FILM BY THE ANTI-THEFT CAMERAS! PATRONS OF THE ARTS FLEE FOR THEIR LIVES!

HUNDREDS OF PRICELESS PAINTINGS ARE RIPPED TO SHREDS IN THE AWFUL RAMPAGE! WEALTHY BENEFACTORS ARE TRAMPLED! THE MUSEUM IS IN RUINS! ON TO SYMPHONY HALL!!

CALVIN? ... CALVIN? WE'RE IN THE NEXT ROOM NOW. C'MON.

I THINK WE'D BETTER GET HIM OUT OF HERE. HE HAD THAT GRIN AGAIN.

I WANNA SEE THE DINOSAURS AT THE NATURAL HISTORY MUSEUM AGAIN.

WE SPENT ALL AFTERNOON THERE, CALVIN.